HAPPINESS HILL

Selected and Edited by
LELAND B. JACOBS
Professor of Education
Teachers College, Columbia University
and
JO JASPER TURNER
Juvenile Editor
Formerly Elementary School
Teacher, Principal, and Supervisor

CHARLES E. MERRILL BOOKS, INC.

Columbus, Ohio

TREASURY OF
BANNER EDITION
LITERATURE

The books in order of difficulty are:

SEESAW
•
MERRY-GO-ROUND
•
HAPPINESS HILL
• •
TREAT SHOP
• • •
MAGIC CARPET
• • • •
ENCHANTED ISLES
• • • • •
ADVENTURE LANDS
• • • • • •

CHARLES E. MERRILL BOOKS, INC.
1300 ALUM CREEK DRIVE • COLUMBUS, OHIO

CONTENTS

OUT IN THE OPEN

Illustrated by Harold Berson

CLEVER ANIMALS

Illustrated by Susan Perl

WITS AND WISHES

Illustrated by Bernice Myers

JUST SUPPOSE

Illustrated by Gordon Laite and Catherine Scholz

6

Now I Know

Now I know what's happening,
  What's happening, what's happening.
Now I know what's happening—
  I've taken time to look.

Now I know what's happening,
  What's happening, what's happening.
Now I know what's happening—
  I've read it in my book.

                    —*Leland B. Jacobs*

I Met a Man

I met a man that was very wise.
He had no hands,
  but he had three eyes,
One green, one yellow, and one red.
He had nothing at all
  but eyes in his head.

He looked at me
  and kept winking and winking
As if to say,
  "Guess what I'm thinking."

—You're making it up! It isn't so!

—Oh, yes it is.
  He is someone you know.
He lives on my street,
  and he can't talk
But he knows how to say
  STOP, GO, and WALK.
And that's all he says,
  all day and all night.

—Oh, now I know!
MR. TRAFFIC LIGHT!

John Ciardi

The Wee Little House

Patricia Scarry

A wee little house sits alone
in the woods.
In the house lives a wee little man.
"I live all alone," says
the wee little man.
But he only thinks he does.

In a tiny hole, in the wee little
house, lives a fat little,
gray little mouse.

And nobody knows that he lives
there—nobody else but the mouse.

Just under the roof live three gray
squirrels.

By the window is a robin's nest.

Snug under the step is
a fat raccoon.

And under the porch a small rabbit
lives.

Yes, they all have homes
in the wee little house.

But the wee little man
never sees them.

And the wee little man
never hears them.

"I live all alone," says
the wee little man.

But he only thinks he does.

Jump or Jiggle

Frogs jump.
Caterpillars hump.

Worms wiggle.
Bugs jiggle.

Rabbits hop.
Horses clop.

Snakes slide.
Sea gulls glide.

Puppies bounce.
Kittens pounce.

Lions stalk—
But
I walk!

Evelyn Beyer

Uncle Frank

It's queer about my Uncle Frank,
He sits and figures in a bank,
When he might keep a candy store—
A shining sign above the door.
Or he might keep a big toy shop
With things that fly and skip and hop—
With trailer trucks and things that crank,
Instead of working in a bank.

Monica Shannon

The Doorman

The doorman stands erect
        And stiff
As long as he's at work.
        But if
You wait until his work
        Is through
He's glad to play a game
        With you.

Marchette Chute

City Boy

Miriam Schlein

A boy stood on a bridge
and looked down on the city.
"I live where I live—I love
where I live," the boy said.

Do you know who he was? He was a
city boy. It was the end of the day.
It was getting dark. He saw the tug
boats come back up the river.

He saw the big tall buildings stick
up in the sky with little white dots
of light in their sides.

And as he watched the city shadows,
this is what he said:

I see the ships come up the river.
Where do they come from? Where will
they go? I stand and watch, and I
never know.

I walk through the market early in the morning. All kinds of cars are there, and all kinds of trucks— with piles of grapefruit, stacks of lettuce, wet and green, and fresh.

I go to the airport and see the planes. Brr, Brr, warm up motors. Brr, Brr, roll down field. Brr, Brr, go down the runway, go up in the air and fly away—high in the clouds, over the land and sea.

I watch the men building a building.
They dig a hole in the ground. They
pour cement. They lay the bricks.
They put in the pipes.

Sometimes I go to the museum. I see
the skeletons of dinosaurs that lived
millions of years ago. I see spears and
arrowheads of Indians. I see stuffed
animals that almost look alive.

But the nicest thing about the city is all the wonderful people. They come from all over the world.

They all live in the city, and I live there, too. I know they are all nice.

Things come from all over the world to my city. Things go to all over the world from my city.

I think my city is in the middle of the world.

I live where I live. I love where I live. I'm the boy from the city.

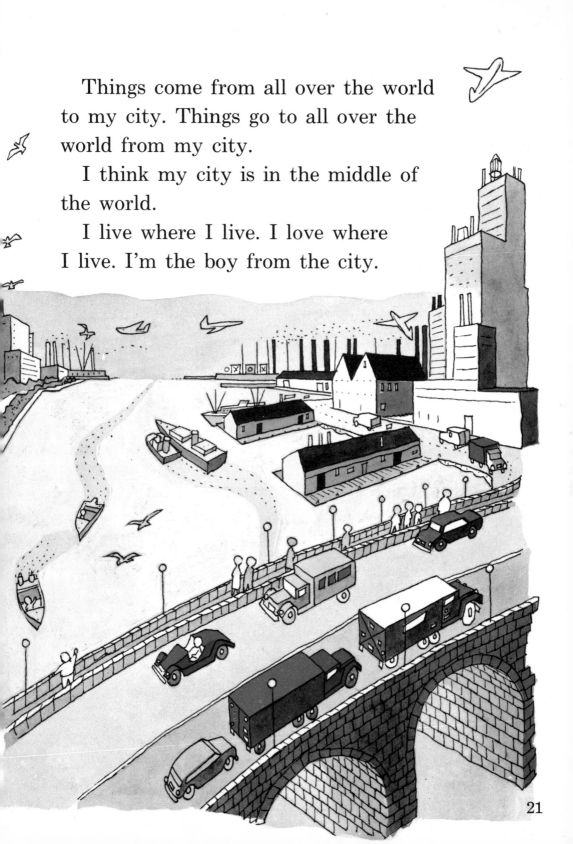

Rain Drop Splash

Drip drop *splash!*
Drip drop *splash!*
   Went the rain all day.
Dripped
   from the shiny leaves,
Dropped
   from a rabbit's nose,
Splashed
   from a brown bear's tail.
Fell from a daisy's face,
Trickled down the tree trunks,
And *splunked*
   on a green frog's back!

Alvin Tresselt

Going Somewhere

Let's go somewhere!
 Where shall it be?
Out beyond the moon and stars?
 Far across the sea?

Let's go somewhere
 Not so far away,
The park, or hill, or any place
 Where we can run and play.
 —*Leland B. Jacobs*

A Sack of Potatoes

Rita S. Cooper

One very bright morning
Joe Jones came down the street
bumping a sack of potatoes
very close to his feet.
　Joe skipped and he jumped,
right over a hump,
and suddenly, *thump!*
The sack dumped—
and out rolled the potatoes!
　They rolled and they rolled and
they rolled, bumpety, bump, bump.

One rolled into Mr. Alec's
drugstore—bump, behind a pill box.

Two rolled into Mr. Sammy's
shoe store—bump, over a sandal.

Three rolled into Mr. Andy's
market—bump, under some apples.

Four rolled into Mr. Philip's
fish store—bump, next to a flounder.

Five rolled into Mr. Walter's
toy store—bump, bump, brrump,
onto a wagon.

Out hurried Mr. Alec,
with one potato in his hand.
Out hurried Mr. Sammy,
with one potato in each hand.
Out hurried Mr. Andy,
with three potatoes in his hands.
Out hurried Mr. Philip,
with three potatoes in his hands
and one in his pocket.

Out hurried Mr. Walter,
with three potatoes in his hands
and two in his pockets.

Joe sang, "Oh, there they are!"
and stuffed them back into the sack,
one after the other.

And down the street he went
with the sack of potatoes
bumping very close to his feet,
that very bright morning.

One Kitten for Kristy

Adelaide Holl

Kristy was a girl who had too many kittens. Kristy did not think so, but her mother and father did.

"You may keep just one kitten," they told her. "You will have to give the rest of them away. We just can't have a house full of kittens."

Kristy chose the roundest polka dot kitten for her own. She put the others in a basket and set it in her wagon. Then away she went with FIVE kittens in her basket.

Mrs. McGinty was sweeping her
walk. "What beautiful kittens!"
she said, looking into the basket.

"Would you like one?" Kristy
asked.

"Indeed I would!" said Mrs.
McGinty. "But you see,
I have some goldfish.
A kitten might eat the goldfish."

"Maybe we could trade," said Kristy.

Mrs. McGinty hurried inside.
She came out with a round glass bowl.
In it were two golden-orange fish.

Kristy was delighted.

Mrs. McGinty chose a kitten of
snowball-white. She set the goldfish
in the wagon. Away Kristy went
with FOUR kittens in her basket,
and two goldfish in a bowl.

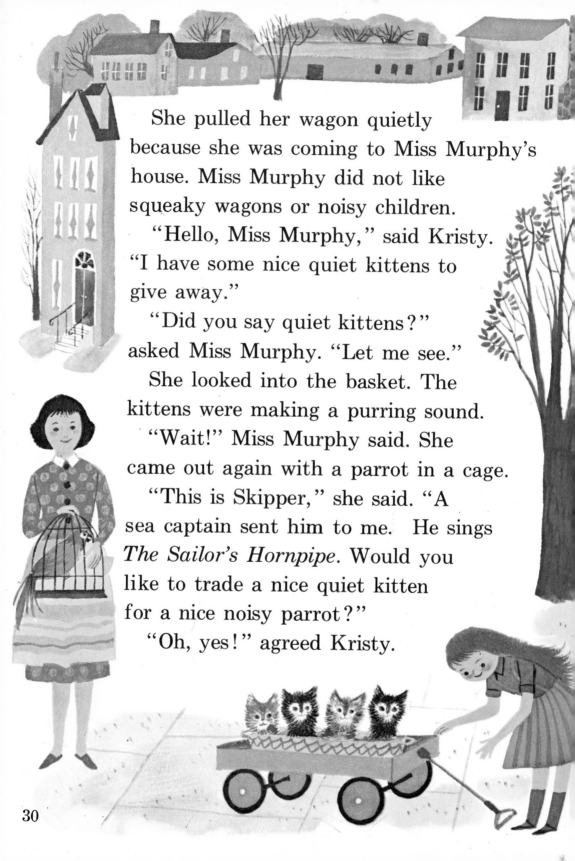

She pulled her wagon quietly because she was coming to Miss Murphy's house. Miss Murphy did not like squeaky wagons or noisy children.

"Hello, Miss Murphy," said Kristy. "I have some nice quiet kittens to give away."

"Did you say quiet kittens?" asked Miss Murphy. "Let me see."

She looked into the basket. The kittens were making a purring sound.

"Wait!" Miss Murphy said. She came out again with a parrot in a cage.

"This is Skipper," she said. "A sea captain sent him to me. He sings *The Sailor's Hornpipe*. Would you like to trade a nice quiet kitten for a nice noisy parrot?"

"Oh, yes!" agreed Kristy.

Miss Murphy chose a kitten of pussy-willow gray.

Away went Kristy down the street with THREE kittens in a basket, two goldfish in a bowl, and one green parrot in a cage.

Kristy turned the corner and stopped to watch Mr. Wiggins. He was making mounds of oranges and apples on his fruit stand.

"Pesky mice!" Mr. Wiggins muttered. "They keep nibbling my fruits and cheeses!"

"What you need is a kitten," Kristy told him.

Mr. Wiggins said, "I could use
two kittens." He picked up two
that were midnight-black. He smiled.
"Come, Kristy. Come with me."

Behind the store was a boxful of
wriggly brown puppies. "Take
your pick," Mr. Wiggins said.

Kristy chose the puppy with the
floppiest ears and the droopiest tail.

And away she went with
ONE kitten in her basket,
two goldfish in a bowl,
one green parrot in a cage,
and a wriggly brown puppy in a box.

She stopped at Mr. Green's house.
He was chasing a shiny black rooster.

"Pesky rooster!" he shouted. "I'm
going to put him in the soup pot!
Every morning, he crows and
wakes me up!"

"Oh, please don't!" called Kristy. "Give him to me. I'll give you a kitten."

Mr. Green looked pleased. "That's a fine idea," he said. "My little girl would love this striped kitten for her birthday tomorrow."

He put the rooster in a small crate. And away Kristy went
with an empty basket,
two goldfish in a bowl,
one green parrot in a cage,
a wriggly brown puppy in a box,
and a shiny black rooster in a crate.

She felt very happy and very proud. When she got home she called, "Mother! Father! I found a home for every single kitten! Aren't you glad?"

The Weather Story

Snow falls down
And covers the ground,
And where is the boy
who is walking?

The sun shines hot
On a sunny spot,
And where is the boy
who is walking?

Fog drifts in from over the sea,
Gray and soft and quietly,
And where is the boy
who is walking?

 From "The Little Weather Story" in READ ME ANOTHER STORY, compiled by the Child Study Association of America. Copyright 1949 by Thomas Y. Crowell Company, New York, publishers.

The sunset reddens the evening sky,
Reddens the barn and the old pigsty,
 And where is the boy
  who is walking?

The night comes softly all around,
Dark in the sky and dark
 on the ground,
 And *here* is the boy who is walking.

Margaret Wise Brown

Singing-Time

I wake in the morning early
And always, the very first thing,
I poke out my head and
  I sit up in bed
And I sing and I sing and I sing.

Rose Fyleman

Susan Blue

Oh, Susan Blue,
  How do you do?
Please may I go for a walk with you?
  Where shall we go?
  Oh, I know—
Down in the meadow
  Where the cowslips grow!

Kate Greenaway

The Big, Big World

Marion Conger

One day after school Chip set out
to see the world.

He followed his feet to the end
of the street and came to a meadow.

"Hello," said Chip to a rabbit
in the meadow. "Which way do I go
to see the world?"

"This meadow is world enough
for me," said the rabbit. "Follow
your nose if you want to see more."

In the meadow Chip picked a blade
of grass to chew on. He picked
some sweet clover for his mother.

Then he followed his nose till he
came to a farm.

"Hello," said Chip to a goose
in the farmyard. "Which way do I go
to see the world?"

"This farm is world enough
for me," said the goose, shaking
its feathers. "Follow the wind
if you want to see more."

Chip wet his finger and held it up
to see which way the wind was
blowing. He picked up a white goose
feather and put it in his pocket.

Then he followed the wind. He
followed it till he came to a brook.

"Hello," Chip said to a fish
in the brook. "Which way do I go
to see the world?"

"This brook is world enough
for me," said the fish, leaping
from the water. "Follow the brook
if you want to see more."

Chip took off his shoes and
his socks. He waded into the brook.
He picked up some pebbles and
put them in his pocket.

He followed the brook
till he came to a woods.

"Hello," said Chip to a squirrel.
"Which way do I go to see
the world?"

"These woods are world enough
for me," said the squirrel, dropping
a nut. "Follow the trees if you want
to see more."

Chip picked up the nut and put it
in his pocket. Then he followed
the trees till he came to a road.

A nest full of baby birds was
by the side of the road.

"Hello," said Chip
to the mother bird. "Which way
do I go to see the world?"

"This nest is world enough for me,"
said the mother bird. "But follow
the sun if you want to see more."

Chip picked a red berry from the bush and put it in his pocket. Then he followed the sun down the road.

The sun was getting lower and lower and lower in the sky. And Chip was getting hungrier and hungrier and hungrier. The world seemed like a very big place indeed.

Then the sun began to sink behind the hills. Chip hurried. He followed the sinking sun till he came to a street.

Down the street came the smell of fried chicken. Chip followed the smell to his own house.

"Hello," said Chip's mother.
"Where have you been? It is
almost dark."

"I have been out to see the world,"
said Chip. "It is a very big place."

Chip put his hand in his pocket. "I
found many things in the big world,"
said Chip. "I have clover from the
meadow, and a feather from a goose,
and some pebbles from the brook. I
have a nut from the woods and a red
berry from a bush. They are all for
you!"

"What beautiful gifts!" said
Chip's mother. Then she said, "You
must be very hungry after your trip."

And, of course, Chip was very
hungry after such a long trip.

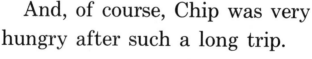

The Wonderful Feast

Esphyr Slobodkina

Early in the morning, Farmer Jones got up and said, "It is a beautiful morning. The sun is shining bright. The birds are singing, and I feel fine!"

Then he went into the barn and gave his horse a great big breakfast.

"My," said the old horse. "What a wonderful feast I'm going to have!"

He ate all he wanted and went to sleep. Then everything was quiet again.

43

A goat came into the barn.
She looked at what was left
of the horse's meal.

"My, oh, my!" she said. "What
a wonderful feast I'm going to have!"

She ate all she wanted and left
the barn.

Just then the hen came in
looking for breakfast.

"Children, children," she called.
"Look what a wonderful feast we are
going to have!"

In a moment the floor was covered
with little chicks, having

their breakfast.

All was quiet again in the barn
after they left.

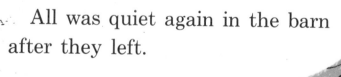

"Oh, my—oh, my—oh, my!" whispered a little mouse, peeping out of his hole. "What a wonderful feast I'm going to have!"

He crossed the floor to where the grains lay and took all he could to his house.

Then a busy old ant came into the barn. He picked up the last grain and took it away. "My, oh, my!" said the ant. "What a wonderful feast I'm going to have!"

Big Is a City

A city is buildings
Scraping the sky;
My neck gets tired
Of looking so high.

A city is people
Crowding the street—
One million faces,
Two million feet.

Dorothy Hall Smith

46

Little Is a Town

The little town has houses,
Two churches and a store,
A school and service station—
There isn't room for more.

Close around the houses,
The hills stand green and bright.
They guard the little town by day
And tuck it in at night.

Dorothy Hall Smith

47

The Dog and the Rooster

Old Tale

One day a dog and a rooster who
were very good friends started out
to see the world. Before they had
gone very far, it began to grow dark.

"Let us stay here for the night,"
said the rooster. "I can roost
on the lowest branch of this tree, and
you can sleep in the hollow trunk."

"That will be fine," said the dog.

So the rooster flew up to his branch,
and the dog curled up in his hole.
They both went to sleep.

In the morning the rooster woke up
early and began to crow,
"Cock-a-doodle-do! Cock-a-doodle-do!"

A fox off in the woods heard him.

"That is a rooster crowing," the fox
said to himself. "He will make
a fine breakfast for me."

So the fox followed the sound
of the crowing. Soon he could see
the rooster up in the tree.

"Cock-a-doodle-do!" said the rooster.

"Ha, what a fine breakfast he will be
for me!" said the fox. "Now I must
make him come down from that tree."

So the fox said to the rooster,
"What a fine rooster you are! How
well you crow! Will you come
to my house for breakfast?"

"Thank you," said the rooster.
"I will be glad to come if my friend
may come, too."

The fox was pleased. Now he would
have two fine roosters to eat!

"Oh, yes," said the fox. "I will be glad to have your friend come. Where is he?"

"My friend is sleeping in the trunk of this tree," said the rooster. "Just wake him up."

"Oh, this is fine," thought the fox.

So he put his head into the hole in the tree trunk and said, "Will you come to my house for breakfast?"

"Yes," said the dog. Then out he jumped and caught the fox by the nose.

51

I Went for a Walk

I went for a walk
And what did I see?
The sun in the sky
Shining down on me.

Houses in yards
All along the way,
People on the sidewalk,
Happy and gay.

A woman walked by,
A man came too;
A dog wagged his tail,
A cat said mew.

Everybody smiled,
Happy as could be,
Going for a walk—
Just like me!

Lois Lenski

Out in the Open

Out in the open,
   High, so high,
Airplane, bird, and butterfly.

Out in the open,
   Far, so far,
Mountain top and evening star.

Out in the open,
   Free, so free,
Shadow, wind, my dog, and me.

—*Leland B. Jacobs*

A Cowboy's Day

Clyde Robert Bulla

Danny was visiting Uncle Mack's ranch. There were six cowboys on the ranch. One of them was named Slim. He had red hair and freckles.

Danny asked Slim, "What does a cowboy do all day?"

Slim said, "You can ride with me tomorrow. You can see what a cowboy does all day."

The next morning Slim rode a white horse. Danny rode a spotted pony. Shep, the collie dog, ran with them.

"Where are we going?" asked Danny.

"We are going to drive some cattle to the mountains, where the grass is green," said Slim.

They rode over a hill. At the foot of the hill was a water hole. All around the water hole were white-faced cattle.

"Hey! Hey!" shouted Slim. "Get along there." Shep barked, and the cattle began to move away from the water hole.

The mountains did not look far away, but it was nearly dark when they got there.

"This is a good place for the cattle," said Slim. "It has plenty of grass and water. We'll camp here tonight."

Danny looked around. He saw a log
cabin under the trees. They tied their
horses under the trees and went into
the cabin. In the cabin were a stove
and a wood box, a table, and two bunks.

"This is a cow camp," said Slim.
"When a cowboy is riding the range,
he stops at a cow camp. We keep
something to eat here. We'll have
a good supper tonight."

After supper, they took off their
boots and went to bed. Shep slept
under one of the bunks.

In the morning they had an early breakfast. Then they cleaned the cabin. Slim cut some wood, and Danny filled the wood box.

"Now everything is ready for the next cowboy," said Slim. "Today we will fix fences on our way back home." They rode away from the camp. Shep ran after them.

"What else does a cowboy do?" Danny asked.

Slim said, "A cowboy does many things. He takes care of his horses. He ropes calves and brands them. Sometimes he shoots a snake."

They rode slowly along the trail. They found several places where the fences were broken. Slim stopped to fix the broken places.

At the bottom of a hill Shep began to bark. Danny looked around. He saw some trees and a pile of rocks.

Danny called, "Slim! A little calf is caught between two big rocks."

Slim came quickly. He moved the rocks. The calf was free, but it could not walk. Slim ran his hand over the calf's leg. "No bones are broken. It was caught in the rocks so long that the feeling has gone out of its foot."

Slim pointed to the brand on the calf. "This is not one of our calves," he said. "It belongs to the Circle-A Ranch. We can stop there on the way home." He showed Danny how to carry the calf on his pony.

They rode until they came to the
Circle-A Ranch. Dogs barked,
and a boy ran out of the house.

"That's my pet calf, Trixie," said
the boy. "Where did you find her?"

"We found her on our ranch,"
said Danny. "Her foot was caught
in the rocks."

The boy took the calf in his arms.
He said, "Thank you for saving
Trixie."

Danny said, "Don't thank me.
Thank Shep. He found the calf
in the rocks."

The Wild White Horse

Retold by Willis Lindquist

At night cowboys like to sit around
a campfire and sing and tell stories.
One of the stories they often tell is
about a wild white horse.

A wild horse it was, with silvery
mane and tail, and it could run faster
than the wind.

A big horse, and smart—and the
most beautiful horse in the world,
cowboys said. Each one that saw
it wanted it for his own.

One cowboy named Tex almost did catch the white horse.

He watched and waited, and one day he saw the horse drinking from a pool. It was a deep pool of spring water.

Tex built a fence around that pool, and he left the gate wide open. Then he hid, and he waited.

But the beautiful white horse was too smart. It saw the fence, and it stopped going to that water hole.

Tex waited. The dry season came, and all the water holes dried up—all except that one, which was fed by springs. Tex waited, for he knew the white horse would soon have to come there to drink.

At last, one day, the horse did
come to the pool. It went right inside
the fence. Tex quickly shut the gate.
Then he gave a whoop—the white
horse was his at last!

The sun had set, and Tex knew that
it was too dark to rope the horse that
night. He would have to wait until
morning.

But in the morning the horse had gone. The great, strong horse had smashed right through the gate!

Sadly, Tex turned away.

Many cowboys had tried to catch the wild horse before, and many more tried after Tex.

But to this day, no one has caught the beautiful white horse. Free and wild it runs—faster than the wind.

The Story That Never Ends

It was a dark and stormy night. Some Indians were sitting around the campfire. Their chief rose and said . . .

It was a dark and stormy night. Some Indians were sitting around the campfire. Their chief rose and said . . .

It was a dark and stormy night. Some Indians were sitting around the campfire. Their chief rose and said . . .

Little Star

Elizabeth Beecher

Little Star was an Indian boy. His full name was Great-Star-in-the-Sky. But everybody on the Canyon Ranch called him Little Star.

One evening Little Star heard Bill Allen talking to one of the cowboys.

"Happy, we'll brand the calves on the north range tomorrow," said Bill. "Tell the boys to be ready to ride at sun-up."

"Okay," said Happy, the cowboy, starting for the bunkhouse.

Bill headed for the barn, and
Little Star ran after him.

"Bill!" called Little Star. "May
I go along to the branding tomorrow?
Please!"

Bill shook his head. "Sorry, son.
It's too dangerous for anybody who
isn't mighty good at roping."

"I'm good," said Little Star.

Again Bill shook his head.

So Little Star sadly walked away.

By sun-up next morning,
Little Star was no longer sad.

He hurried to the corral where the
cowboys were saddling their horses.
Perching on the top of the fence,
he tried to rope their saddle horns.
But all he roped was Happy's hat.

Happy lifted Little Star off the
fence. "You need a good spanking,
little fellow!" he said.

Little Star raced for a tall tree.
He stayed up in the tree until Happy
and Bill and the boys rode off toward
the north range.

Then he slid down and got his rope.
He mounted Clover, his little burro,
and rode after them.

At the north range Little Star
hid up in the rocks. He watched Bill
and the cowboys roping and branding
calves in the meadow below.

Suddenly a calf broke away and
headed straight for Little Star's
hiding place.

Little Star shook out his rope and
waited until the calf came alongside.
He swung his rope right over the
calf's head.

Quickly Little Star pulled the rope tight. But the calf squirmed and twisted and tugged until he pulled Little Star off Clover's back!

Little Star did not let go of the rope.

Soon Bill rode by. His rope flew through the air—and caught that calf!

Happy rode up and took the calf back to the branding fire.

Bill smiled down at Little Star. "That was good roping," he said.

Little Star smiled. He knew that now he could stay at the branding. Then he stopped smiling.

"But, Bill, I'm not really a very good roper," he said. "I let the calf pull me right off Clover's back."

"Don't worry about that," chuckled Bill. "If I hired only cowboys who'd never taken a spill, nobody would be working for me—not even myself!"

How the Chipmunk Got His Stripes

An Old Indian Legend
Retold by Willis Lindquist

Long ago, all the birds and animals met to decide how much light they should have.

"I think we should have light all the time," said Eagle.

"No," said Owl. "Light hurts our eyes. It should be dark all the time."

"No, no!" shouted many animals.

"Owl is right," said Bear. "Hunting is better in the dark. It should always be dark."

Then Chipmunk said, "I think half the day should be dark and the other half should be light."

The other animals thought Chipmunk had the best idea. So they divided the day into a light part and a dark part.

But Bear wanted it all dark. He was so angry at Chipmunk that he chased him. Before Chipmunk could reach his hole, Bear clawed his back, leaving long scratches.

From that day to this, all chipmunks have had long stripes on their backs.

How the Bear Lost His Tail

Retold by Leland B. Jacobs

Mr. Fox lived in the forest.

All the forest animals knew him. They knew he was sly. They knew he played jokes on everybody.

Mr. Bear lived in the forest, too.

All the forest animals knew him. They knew he was slow. They knew he was honest. They knew he trusted everybody.

One winter morning Mr. Bear met
Mr. Fox. Mr. Fox was carrying
a big fish.

Mr. Bear was hungry. He had not
had breakfast. He wanted
a big fish, too.

"What a big fish!" said Mr. Bear.

"Yes, it is a big fish," said Mr. Fox.

"Did you buy it?" asked Mr. Bear.

"No, I caught it," said Mr. Fox.

"I'm hungry," said Mr. Bear. "Could
I catch a fish?"

"Of course you could," said Mr. Fox.
"I'll tell you how. Go to the river.
Cut a hole in the ice. Put your tail
in the hole. Catch a fish on your tail."

Mr. Bear went to the river. He cut
a hole in the ice. He put his tail
in the hole. He sat and sat and sat.
He was hungry.

He sat and sat some more. He was
cold. He sat and sat some more. He
was tired and sleepy. He sat and sat
some more. But Mr. Bear caught no
fish.

Mr. Bear was very tired. He was
very cold. He was very sleepy. He was
very hungry. But he had caught not
one fish.

"I won't sit here any more," said Mr. Bear. He tried to get up. He was frozen fast. His tail was frozen in the ice.

Poor Mr. Bear! He pulled gently. He pulled harder and harder and harder. He was still frozen fast.

Then he gave a great jerk. He was free. But his tail was still frozen in the ice.

To this day, bears don't trust foxes. And all bears have short, small, stubby, stumpy tails.

Clever Animals

I never saw an animal,
 Big or small,
I never saw an animal,
 Short or tall,
I never saw an animal
 Caged or free,
Who wasn't quite clever
 When he wanted to be.

—*Leland B. Jacobs*

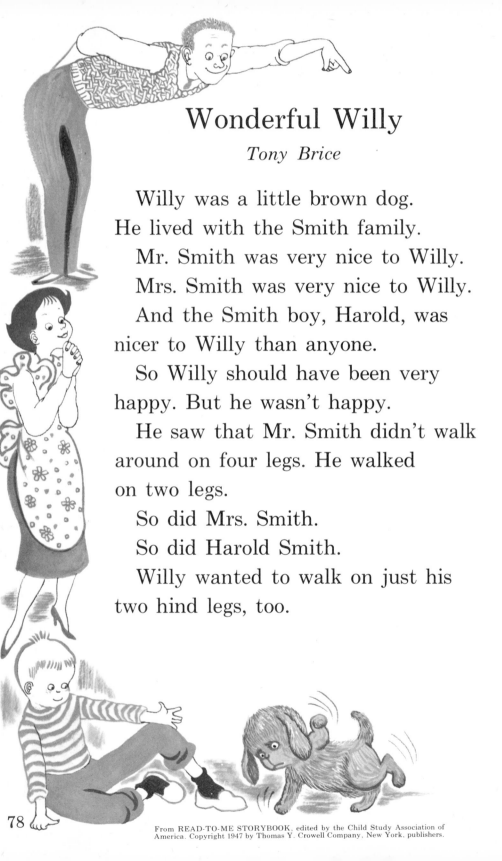

Wonderful Willy

Tony Brice

Willy was a little brown dog.
He lived with the Smith family.

Mr. Smith was very nice to Willy.

Mrs. Smith was very nice to Willy.

And the Smith boy, Harold, was
nicer to Willy than anyone.

So Willy should have been very
happy. But he wasn't happy.

He saw that Mr. Smith didn't walk
around on four legs. He walked
on two legs.

So did Mrs. Smith.

So did Harold Smith.

Willy wanted to walk on just his
two hind legs, too.

78

From READ-TO-ME STORYBOOK, edited by the Child Study Association of America. Copyright 1947 by Thomas Y. Crowell Company, New York, publishers.

He tried and tried to walk on just his hind legs. And at last Willy did!

Mr. Smith saw Willy walking on his hind legs. "How wonderful Willy is!" said Mr. Smith.

"How wonderful Willy is!" said Mrs. Smith.

"How very wonderful Willy is!" shouted Harold Smith.

All the Smiths were very proud of Willy.

They called in their friends and neighbors to see Willy walking around on his hind legs. It was hard work for Willy to walk around on his hind legs. But he didn't mind, because he was so proud and happy.

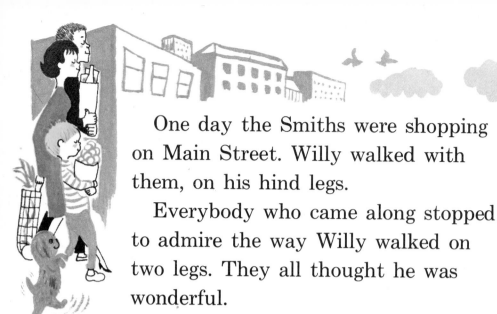

One day the Smiths were shopping on Main Street. Willy walked with them, on his hind legs.

Everybody who came along stopped to admire the way Willy walked on two legs. They all thought he was wonderful.

Just then the kind butcher came out of his shop. He put some bones down on the sidewalk for the dogs.

Dogs came running from everywhere—old dogs, young dogs, black dogs, white dogs, brown dogs, yellow dogs, and spotted dogs! Even a little puppy, who wasn't old enough to eat a bone, ran to the butcher shop.

Willy tried to run on his hind legs.
But he couldn't. He could only walk
slowly.

He wanted a bone so much that at
last he dropped down on all four legs
and *ran*.

It felt so good to be on four legs
again that Willy ran faster than he
had ever run before. He ran so fast
that he reached the butcher shop first
and picked out the biggest bone of all.

When Willy had eaten his bone, he started back to the Smiths. He remembered how proud of him Mr. and Mrs. Smith had been when he walked on just his hind legs.

Willy remembered how very proud Harold Smith had been.

Poor Willy thought the Smiths would be ashamed of him. He had stopped walking on two legs and had run on all four! And right on Main Street in front of all their friends, too!

Willy walked very slowly, with his tail between his legs. He felt very unhappy.

But when Mr. Smith saw Willy, he said, "How wonderful Willy is! He can walk on just his hind legs when he wants to. But when he wants to go fast, he can run faster on all four legs than any other dog."

"How wonderful Willy is!" said Mrs. Smith, too.

"How *very* wonderful Willy is!" shouted Harold Smith.

And from that day on, when Willy walked on his two hind legs, he felt happy.

When he ran on all four legs, he felt happy.

But when he just sat by the fire with Harold Smith, he felt *very* happy.

The Mouse's House

One time there was a woodland mouse
Who lived inside a funny house.
It had no doors,
It had no floors,
The home of Mister Mouse.

The mouse's house was full of weeds,
And bits of grass, and little seeds.
There were no chairs,
There were no stairs,
And yet it seemed to suit his needs.

The little mousies had no bed,
There was no roof top overhead.
There was no clock,
There was no lock,
No lamp (they used the sun instead).

No roof, no lock, no clock, no doors,
No bed, no chairs, no stairs, no floors,
Where was the house
Of Mister Mouse?
Why, in a grassy field outdoors!

Pat Day

Muddy Mouse

Helen and Alf Evers

Every day the Mouse family went for a walk.

When they came to a mud puddle, Father Mouse walked around it. Mother Mouse walked around it. Sister Mouse and Brother Mouse walked around it, too. But little Muddy Mouse walked right through it. He liked mud.

His friend, the horse, didn't like mud. The cow didn't like mud. The dog and the cat didn't like mud. But Muddy Mouse liked mud so much that he cried when there wasn't any.

From READ-TO-ME STORYBOOK, compiled by the Child Study Association of America. Copyright 1947 by Thomas Y. Crowell Company, New York, publishers.

One day Muddy Mouse played
on the muddy pasture road. He rolled
over and over down the road. Muddy
Mouse thought it was fun, because the
road was full of sticky brown mud.

But the mud stuck to his fur! More
and more mud stuck to Muddy Mouse,
until he looked like a big brown ball
of mud. The tip of his tail stuck out
of one side of the ball. The tip of his
nose stuck out of the other side.

There was so much mud on Muddy
Mouse that he couldn't walk. He
couldn't talk. He couldn't even cry,
and he wanted to cry very much.

Just then the black cat and her two
kittens came along.

They thought Muddy Mouse was a
big brown ball, so they started to play
with him. They rolled him back and
forth. They rolled him around and
around, until Muddy Mouse was dizzy.

Then the black cat and her two
kittens gave Muddy Mouse a push.
Away he rolled over the pasture. He
didn't stop until he reached the fence.

After the black cat and her two kittens had scampered away, Father Mouse and Mother Mouse came out to look for Muddy Mouse. They looked under every stone and behind every bush.

But they would never have found Muddy Mouse at all if he hadn't wiggled the tip of his tail to call for help.

Then Father Mouse and Mother Mouse scraped and scraped and scrubbed and scrubbed at the big brown ball of mud.

At last they saw an ear, then a bright little eye, then a smooth gray back.

And after a long, long time there stood Muddy Mouse—all of him. He danced and squeaked with happiness, because he didn't have a single bit of mud on him.

Every day after that, the Mouse family still went for a walk.

And when they came to a mud puddle, Father Mouse still walked around it. Mother Mouse walked around it. Sister Mouse and Brother Mouse walked around the puddle, too.

But Muddy Mouse didn't walk around it. He *ran* around it.

Bird Talk

"Think . . ." said the robin,
"Think . . ." said the jay,
sitting in the garden,
talking one day.

"Think about people—
the way they grow:
they don't have feathers
at all, you know.

"They don't eat beetles,
they don't grow wings,
they don't like sitting
on wires and things."

"Think!" said the robin.
"Think!" said the jay.
"Aren't people funny
to be that way?"

Aileen Fisher

One Cold Day

Elizabeth Coatsworth

One cold day in late fall, a little boy got lost in the woods. The first snow had just started to fall.

He hunted east, he hunted west, but he couldn't find his way out. He hunted north, he hunted south, but he couldn't find a little house with a stove in it.

He looked up and he looked down, but he saw only trees, branches, and fallen leaves.

So he was very happy when he saw someone in a big coat coming through the woods.

The someone turned out to be an old bear in a fur cap and a muffler and mittens.

"Hello," said the old bear. "Lost, eh? Come along with me."

So the little boy went along with the bear. Pretty soon they came to a cave in the rocks. There was a small green door.

The bear opened the door with a key and turned on the lights. Inside, the cave was very cozy. There were two chairs and a table and a big old stove. The fire in the stove crackled merrily. A pot of chocolate stood at the back of the stove. There were cinnamon buns in the oven.

The old bear and the little boy had a very happy hour.

In fact, the bear asked the little boy if he didn't want to spend the winter with him.

"Of course I snooze a lot in the winter," the bear said. "I'll snooze in that chair, and you snooze in this one. We'll have a nice time."

But the little boy wanted to go home and see his family.

So the bear wrapped up again in his big coat, his fur hat, his muffler, and his mittens. This time he put on his overshoes. He took the boy to the edge of the woods and pointed his own house out to him. The windows in the house had just been lighted.

"Oh, thank you," said the little boy, turning to wave. "Good night."

"He means good winter, I guess," said the bear to himself as he walked back into the woods. "Anyway, I mean to sleep all winter!" And he gave a big yawn, and then another.

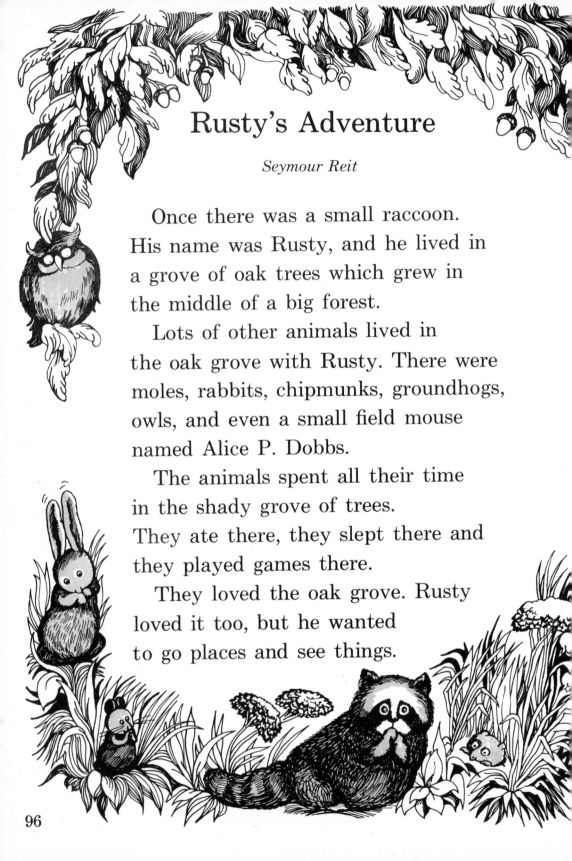

Rusty's Adventure

Seymour Reit

Once there was a small raccoon.
His name was Rusty, and he lived in
a grove of oak trees which grew in
the middle of a big forest.

Lots of other animals lived in
the oak grove with Rusty. There were
moles, rabbits, chipmunks, groundhogs,
owls, and even a small field mouse
named Alice P. Dobbs.

The animals spent all their time
in the shady grove of trees.
They ate there, they slept there and
they played games there.

They loved the oak grove. Rusty
loved it too, but he wanted
to go places and see things.

He said, "Nothing ever happens
here. I'm going off to find
a real adventure."

So he said good-by to the moles,
rabbits, chipmunks, groundhogs, owls,
and Alice P. Dobbs, and off he went.

Rusty looked for an adventure
everywhere. He looked in caves, in
trees, in nests, and in holes. But he
couldn't find a single adventure.

Then one day, while he was
walking in the forest, a large bee
buzzed by. Rusty ran back to the
oak grove as fast as he could go.

The animals were all there,
playing "Ring around the Pine Cone."

Rusty shouted, "A bee chased me!"

The oldest owl shook his head.
"*That's* not a real adventure."

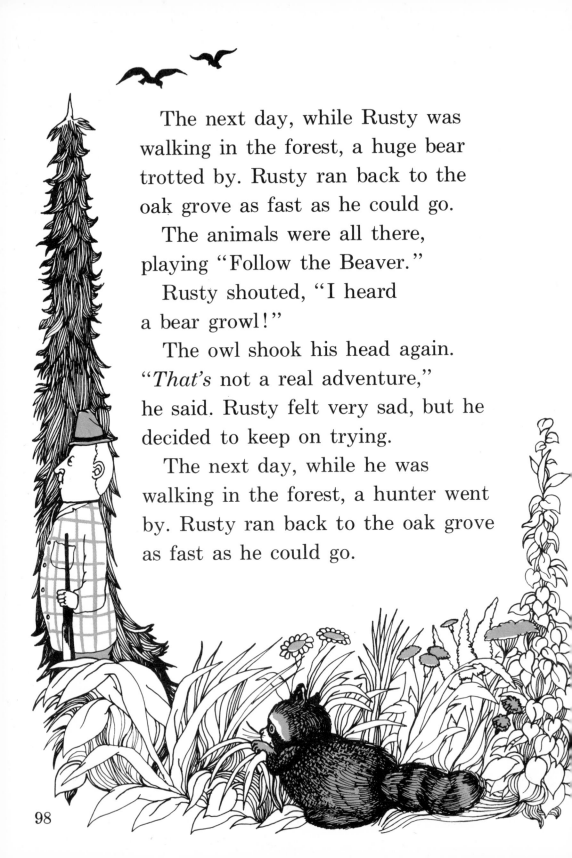

The next day, while Rusty was walking in the forest, a huge bear trotted by. Rusty ran back to the oak grove as fast as he could go.

The animals were all there, playing "Follow the Beaver."

Rusty shouted, "I heard a bear growl!"

The owl shook his head again. "*That's* not a real adventure," he said. Rusty felt very sad, but he decided to keep on trying.

The next day, while he was walking in the forest, a hunter went by. Rusty ran back to the oak grove as fast as he could go.

The animals were all there,
playing "Chipmunk in the Dell."

Rusty shouted, "I saw a hunter!"

The old owl shook his head.
"That's not a real adventure,"
he said. Rusty felt sadder than ever
because he couldn't find an
adventure, no matter how he tried.

The next day he went for a
very long walk in the forest. He
walked farther than ever before,
and the farther he went, the sadder
he became.

Soon he came to a road. On the
road was a big truck. Rusty was
very tired, so he climbed up
on the truck and crawled in the back.
Inside it was cozy and warm. Rusty
sat there resting his paws quietly.

All of a sudden, the truck
began to move. It went faster and
faster! It went so fast that Rusty
was afraid to jump off!

The truck drove until it came
to a big city. Then it stopped, and
the driver began to unload his boxes.

Rusty had never been so scared
in his life. He jumped off the truck
and began to run.

When the driver saw Rusty, he
chased after him. Soon lots of other
people began chasing him.

They chased poor Rusty all over the city. They chased him in and out of stores, through a park, and even into the subway!

Finally they caught him in a big net. Everybody crowded around. A man took Rusty's picture. A dog barked. A policeman wrote things in a little book.

Soon another truck came. The driver put Rusty in a cage and put the cage on the truck. Then he drove out of the big city.

After a long ride, the truck
came to the forest where Rusty lived.
Then the driver opened the cage, and
Rusty raced back to his oak grove.

The animals were all there,
playing "Acorn, Acorn—Who's Got
the Acorn?"

Rusty told them about his ride
and all the other things that had
happened. The animals listened, and
their eyes grew wide with wonder.

The oldest owl smiled.
He said, "Good news, Rusty!
At last, you've had your adventure!"

Angus and the Ducks

Marjorie Flack

Once there was a very young little dog whose name was Angus.

Although the rest of Angus was quite small, his head was very large, and so were his feet.

Angus was curious about many places and many things.

He was curious about *what* lived under the sofa and in dark corners. And *who* was the little dog in the mirror.

He was curious about
Things-Which-Come-Apart and those
Things-Which-Don't-Come-Apart,
such as slippers and gentlemen's
suspenders and things like that.

Angus was also curious about
Things-Outdoors. But he could not
find out much about them
because of a leash.

The leash was fastened at one end
to the collar around his neck and at
the other end to Somebody Else.

But Angus was most curious of all
about a noise which came from the
other side of the large green hedge.

The noise usually sounded like this:
"Quack! Quack! Quackety! Quack!"

But sometimes it sounded like this:
"Quackety! Quackety! Quackety!
Quack!"

One day the door between Outdoors
and Indoors was left open by mistake.
And out went Angus without the
leash or Somebody Else.

Down the path he ran, until he came to the large green hedge.

He tried to go around it, but it was much too long. He tried to go over it, but it was much too high. So Angus went under the large green hedge and came out on the other side.

There, directly in front of him, were two white ducks. They were marching forward, one-foot-up and one-foot-down. "Quack! Quack! Quackety! Quack!"

Angus said, *"Woo-oo-oof!"*

Away went the ducks all of a flutter. "Quackety! Quackety! Quackety! Quackety! Quackety!"

Angus followed after.

Soon the ducks stopped by a stone
watering trough under a mulberry tree.

Angus stopped, too. Each duck
dipped a yellow bill in the clear, cool
water. Angus watched. Each duck
took a long drink of the cool, clear
water. Still Angus watched. Each
duck took another long drink of cool,
clear water.

Then Angus said, *"Woo-oo-oof!"*

Away the ducks scuttled, and
Angus lapped the cool, clear water.

Birds sang in the mulberry tree.

The sun made patterns through the leaves over the grass.

The ducks talked together. "Quack! Quack! Quack!" Then: *"Hiss-s-s-s-s-s-s! Hiss-s-s-s-s-s-s!"*

The first duck nipped Angus's tail! *"Hiss-s-s-s-s-s-s! Hiss-s-s-s-s-s-s!"*

The second duck flapped its wings!

Angus scrambled under the large green hedge, scurried up the path, scampered into the house, and crawled under the sofa. For exactly three minutes by the clock, Angus was *not* curious about anything at all.

The Old Woman and Her Pig

Old Tale

An old woman was cleaning her house when she found a little crooked sixpence. "What shall I do with this little crooked sixpence?" said she. "I will go to market and buy a little pig." So she did.

As she was coming home, she came to a stile. The pig would not go over the stile.

She went a little farther, and she met a dog. So she said to the dog "Dog, bite pig! Pig won't go over the stile, and I shan't get home tonight." But the dog would not.

The old woman went a little farther, and she met a stick. So she said, "Stick, beat dog! Dog won't bite pig. Pig won't go over the stile, and I shan't get home tonight." But the stick would not.

She went a little farther, and she met a fire. So she said, "Fire, burn stick! Stick won't beat dog. Dog won't bite pig. Pig won't go over the stile, and I shan't get home tonight." But the fire would not.

She went a little farther, and she met some water. So she said, "Water, put out fire! Fire won't burn stick. Stick won't beat dog. Dog won't bite pig. Pig won't go over the stile, and I shan't get home tonight." But the water would not.

She went a little farther, and she met an ox. So she said, "Ox, drink water! Water won't put out fire. Fire won't burn stick. Stick won't beat dog. Dog won't bite pig. Pig won't go over the stile, and I shan't get home tonight." But the ox would not.

She went a little farther, and she met a butcher. So she said, "Butcher, kill ox! Ox won't drink water. Water won't put out fire. Fire won't burn stick. Stick won't beat dog. Dog won't bite pig. Pig won't go over the stile, and I shan't get home tonight." But the butcher would not.

The old woman went a little farther, and she met a rope. So she said, "Rope, hang butcher! Butcher won't kill ox. Ox won't drink water. Water won't put out fire. Fire won't burn stick. Stick won't beat dog. Dog won't bite pig. Pig won't go over the stile, and I shan't get home tonight." But the rope would not.

She went a little farther, and she met a rat. So she said, "Rat, chew rope. Rope won't hang butcher. Butcher won't kill ox. Ox won't drink water. Water won't put out fire. Fire won't burn stick. Stick won't beat dog. Dog won't bite pig. Pig won't go over the stile, and I shan't get home tonight." But the rat would not.

She went a little farther, and she
met a cat. So she said, "Cat, kill rat.
Rat won't chew rope. Rope won't
hang butcher. Butcher won't kill ox.
Ox won't drink water. Water won't
put out fire. Fire won't burn stick.
Stick won't beat dog. Dog won't bite
pig. Pig won't go over the stile, and
I shan't get home tonight."

Then the cat said to her, "If you
will go to yonder cow and get me
a saucer of milk, I will kill the rat."

So away went the old woman to the
cow.

But the cow said to her, "Go to
yonder haystack and get me some hay.
Then I will give you the milk."

So away went the woman to the
haystack. She brought the hay to the
cow.

As soon as the cow had eaten the
hay, she gave the old woman the milk.
Away went the old woman with a
saucer of milk for the cat.

The cat lapped up the milk and
began to kill the rat. The rat began
to chew the rope. The rope began to
hang the butcher. The butcher began
to kill the ox. The ox began to drink
the water. The water began to put out
the fire. The fire began to burn the
stick. The stick began to beat the
dog. The dog began to bite the pig.
The little pig in a fright jumped
over the stile, and so the old woman
got home that night.

The Cow

The friendly cow all red and white,
   I love with all my heart:
She gives me cream, with all her might,
   To eat with apple-tart.

She wanders lowing here and there,
   And yet she cannot stray,
All in the pleasant open air,
   The pleasant light of day;

And blown by all the winds that pass
   And wet with all the showers,
She walks among the meadow grass
   And eats the meadow flowers.

Robert Louis Stevenson

Wits and Wishes

If your wits are sharp,
   And you know what to do,
You can make your wishes
   All come true!

        —*Barbara Shook Hazen*

Peter and the Pigeons

Charlotte Zolotow

Peter loved pigeons.

He loved the soft, slow cooooo-oooo sound they made.

He loved the silver-gray color of their feathers.

He loved the way they sat on statues and hid in the carved arches of church doors.

He loved to see them sitting like a row of round, dark plums in the branches of the trees.

He loved to see them flying high and wild, in great, sweeping circles. He loved to see them fluttering back to earth again.

They were his friends.

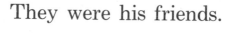

"If you love pigeons so much," his father said, "we must go to the zoo. You will like the animals there. They are strange animals you have never seen before."

So Peter's father took Peter to the zoo.

"See which animal you like best," his father said.

Peter looked at the lion. He was big and kingly. Peter watched him pacing up and down in his cage.

"I don't like him," said Peter.

Peter looked at the brown camel.
He looked at his great bony humps
and his hunched way of walking
forward.

"Not him," Peter said.

Peter looked at the red fox, with his
pointed ears and quick, catlike walk.

"Him?" said Peter's father.

"No," said Peter, "not him. Not the
fox."

Peter looked at the zebras. They were like little, striped, white ponies. There was a baby zebra who looked back at Peter. Peter looked at him for a long time.

"Him, I bet," said Peter's father.

But Peter said, "No, not him."

Peter looked at the big white polar bears. Two lay on a rock by a caged-in waterfall and looked like big white rugs.

"Not you," said Peter to the bears.

Peter looked at the seals. They had small, whiskered, pointy faces, and their black coats shone in the sunlight.

"Them?" asked Peter's father.

"No," said Peter, "not them."

Peter looked at the huge, wrinkled hippopotamus. It had small, black, ugly eyes.

"Not him," said Peter. "I don't like him."

Peter looked at a great gray elephant with a long trunk and gentle eyes.

"Nor him," said Peter, "but he's nice."

Now they had seen everything
in the zoo.

Peter and his father had started
home when Peter suddenly said, *"Him!
I like him the best."*

Peter's father stopped. He looked
where Peter was looking.

A small, silver-gray pigeon was
crossing the path.

Then Peter's father began to laugh.

"Of course," he said at last.
"I should have known."

The Wish

Each birthday wish
I've ever made
Really does come true.
Each year I wish
I'll grow some more
And every year
I do!

Ann Friday

Everybody Says

Everybody says
I look just like my mother.
Everybody says
I'm the image of Aunt Bee.
Everybody says
My nose is like my father's,
But I want to look like *me.*

Dorothy Aldis

My Other Name

Jennifer's my other name.
   (It's make-believe
   and just a game.)

I'm really Anne,
But just the same
I'd much
   much
   rather
   have a name
   like Jennifer.

(So, if you can
   don't call me Anne.)

Myra Cohn Livingston

Fifteen Bathtubs

Margaret Wise Brown

Once there was a little boy who lived in a house with fifteen bathtubs in it. You might think that this little boy was the cleanest little boy in the world, with fifteen bathtubs. But he wasn't.

He was the dirtiest little boy in the world. He hated to wash and he never used even one of the fifteen bathtubs.

Of course, he did take a bath once a month. But when he did take a bath, he used the garden hose. This dirty boy would run right through the water from the hose. That was the only way he took a bath, except when he took a sun bath.

He never got into one of the fifteen bathtubs.

From the book ANOTHER HERE AND NOW STORYBOOK by Lucy Sprague Mitchell. Copyright 1937 by E. P. Dutton & Co., Inc. Reprinted by permission of the publishers.

One morning the little boy got up from the breakfast table, where he had been eating jam on toast. He wiped the jam across his face with the back of his hand. Then he went out into the garden.

Now this was a clean, shining morning. All the animals were out in the warm sun.

The rabbits hopped about, and the squirrels hopped about. The butterflies flew, and the bees went buzzing all around.

So the little boy lay down to take a sun bath. He turned his jam-sticky face up to the sky and closed his eyes.

The bees buzzed in the flowers. They flew through the air looking for something sweet to make into honey. Then they found the little boy's jam-sticky face.

The little boy was asleep. Bzzzzzzzzz. A sticky treasure!

Suddenly many bees were flying all around the little boy's face. Zoom. Szzzz. They buzzed about his nose and lips. Bzzzzz. They buzzed nearer to his cheek. Szzzzz. Buzzz. They were after the sticky, sweet jam on his face.

The little boy jumped awake and he jumped to his feet and he jumped away. But the bees came buzzing all around right after him, trying to get the jam.

He ran and he ran, but still the bees came buzzing after him.

He ran all around the garden, and the bees buzzed all around the garden after him.

He ran and he ran into a field, and the bees buzzed through the field after him.

He ran and he ran and he ran through a wood, and the bees came buzzing after him.

Then he ran and he ran down the black tar road. The bees buzzed down the black tar road after him.

He ran and he ran up the gray gravel driveway. The bees came buzzing up the gray gravel driveway after him.

When he got to his house, he ran in the open front door. The bees came buzzing in the open front door after him.

He ran up the stairs, and the bees came buzzing up the stairs after him.

When he got to the fifteen
bathrooms, he jumped into one
bathtub
and into another bathtub
and another bathtub
and another bathtub
and another bathtub
and another bathtub
and another bathtub
and another bathtub.
He jumped fifteen times, into all
fifteen bathtubs.
Then the bees flew out the window
and back to the flowers in the garden.
They never chased the little boy again.
From that day on, he was just
as clean as the sunlight.

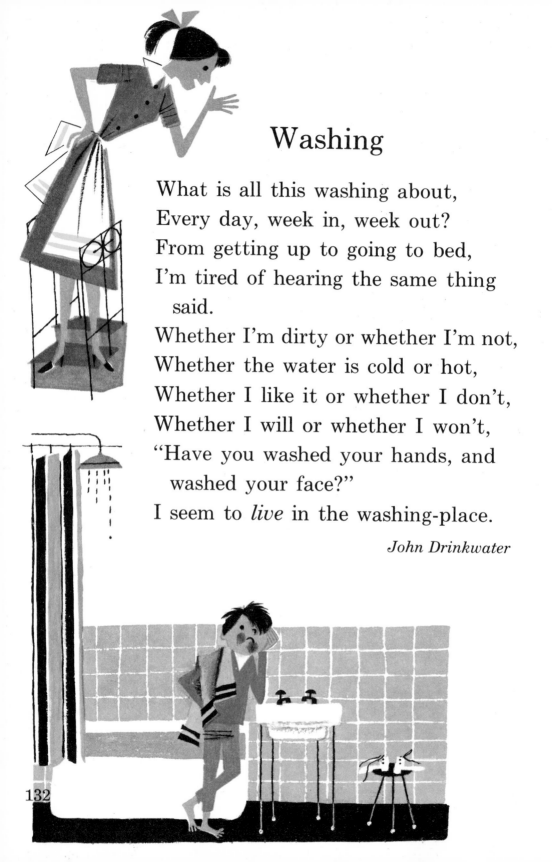

Washing

What is all this washing about,
Every day, week in, week out?
From getting up to going to bed,
I'm tired of hearing the same thing
    said.
Whether I'm dirty or whether I'm not,
Whether the water is cold or hot,
Whether I like it or whether I don't,
Whether I will or whether I won't,
"Have you washed your hands, and
    washed your face?"
I seem to *live* in the washing-place.

John Drinkwater

The New Little Boy

A new little boy moved in next door
So I climbed a tree and bounced on a limb
And asked where he used to live before
And he didn't know but his name was Tim,
So I told all three of my names to him.

When he didn't say anything after that
I hung by my knees to see if he scared
And meowed and made my face like a cat,
But he only stood in his yard and stared,
He only watched like he never cared.

Well, all I know is his name is Tim
And I don't think very much of him.

Harry Behn

Daisy the Dinosaur

Marion Conger

On his way home from school one day, John met a dinosaur. The dinosaur was eating daisies by the side of the road.

She wagged her tail, so John held out a piece of candy. The dinosaur ate right out of his hand.

"Come home with me," said John. "I'll give you some more candy." So the dinosaur followed John home.

John's mother was in the kitchen. "Hello, dear," she said. "What happened in school today?"

"Oh, nothing," John said. "But on the way home I found a dinosaur. I'd like to keep her for a pet."

"First you wanted a collie," said his mother. "Then a great Dane. Now a dinosaur. What next?"

John could see his mother thought he was joking. But just then the dinosaur put her head through the open window.

"I promised her some candy," John said.

John's mother was too surprised to say anything. But she took a piece of candy from the shelf and held it out. The dinosaur ate it all up.

"What else do dinosaurs eat?" asked John's mother.

"This one eats weeds and daisies," said John. "I'd like to call her Daisy."

Then John knew his mother was going to let him keep Daisy because she said, "Well, she'll be easier to feed than a collie or a great Dane."

Next morning John took Daisy to school. His teacher was so excited she held class in the schoolyard so that everybody could study Daisy.

After that, on school days, Daisy
stayed at home. She was very good
about this for a few days.

Then one day she went for a walk.
Passing Mrs. Johnson's house,
she saw a beautiful bed of daisies.
They were Mrs. Johnson's pride and
joy, but they smelled good to Daisy.
They smelled so good she ate them
all up.

Mrs. Johnson was very angry. She
told John's mother she would call the
police if Daisy ever got loose again.

John had to scold Daisy. Even
though dinosaurs have tiny brains,
she seemed to know
what he meant.

That night John woke to hear fire engines clanging down his street. They passed John's house. They went on to Mrs. Johnson's house.

John got dressed and raced down the street. Daisy stayed in the yard.

Poor Mrs. Johnson! Flames were pouring out of her house. And there she was at a third-floor window calling for help. The firemen were trying to get their big ladder up to the third floor. But it was stuck!

Away ran John. Back he came with Daisy at his heels.

"Put your head in Mrs. Johnson's window, Daisy," he said. "Then she can slide down your back."

So Daisy put her head in the upstairs window, and Mrs. Johnson slid down. Whoosh! She slid down to the ground. She gave Daisy a great big hug, and everybody cheered.

Now Daisy goes to all the fires,
right behind the Chief's car. "It's good
to have her along," he says.

Mrs. Johnson planted a lot of new
daisies, and every day she brings Daisy
a bunch. "After all," says
Mrs. Johnson, "she saved my life."

Daisy always stays in the yard now,
except when there's a fire. And every
night she puts her head in John's
window so he can pat her good night.
She is very happy, and John is very
very proud of her.

The Young Deer, the Young Tiger, and the Fox

An Old Chinese Tale
Retold by Barbara Shook Hazen

A young deer was eating grass in a forest high above the Yellow River.

It was summer. Everything was dry. Both the grass and the coat of the deer were dull yellow. It was hard to see the deer when he moved.

But a young tiger saw the deer. He hid behind a rock and watched him.

The young tiger had never before left the cave where he was born.

He had never seen a deer before. But he knew without being told that here was something good to eat.

The young tiger walked up to the deer. The deer was afraid. He wanted to run away. Then he thought, "I would be smarter to stay where I am."

"Of what use," asked the young tiger, "are the horns on your head?"

"Oh," said the young deer, "I use them to spear tigers for my dinner."

The young tiger shook with fear.

Then he asked, "Of what use are the white spots on your body?"

"Oh," said the young deer, "they show how many tigers I have eaten. Every time I kill a tiger, a white spot appears. Shall I show you all the white spots on my other side?"

When the young tiger heard this, he ran away. He ran so fast that his orange fur looked like fire.

A fox saw the young tiger running. He called, "Where are you going in such a hurry?"

The young tiger stopped running. He told the fox what the deer had said.

"You are a silly young tiger," said the fox. "The deer was only trying to trick you. Do not be afraid of him. Go back again!"

"I will not go back!" said the young tiger. "The deer will drive his horns into me. He will kill me. I know he will!"

"Then I will go back with you," said the fox. "You must let me ride on your back."

So the young tiger let the fox ride on his back. He carried the fox back into the forest above the Yellow River.

When he saw the fox and the young tiger, the young deer was even more afraid.

He wanted to run away. Then he thought, "I would be smarter to stay where I am."

The young deer called out in a loud voice, "Big Brother Fox, you promised me a tiger. The one you brought today looks good to eat, even if it is just a young tiger. I see you keep your promise, and I thank you."

When the young tiger heard this, he was sure the fox had tricked him.

He ran to the cliff. He shook the fox from his back right—splash!—into the Yellow River.

Then he ran all the way back to his cave.

The young deer was safe. He held his head high. His horns were sharp, but his wits were even sharper.

Seventeen Nephews

Kathryn and Byron Jackson

Once there was a big sailor with a
merry twinkle in his bright blue eyes.

"I have seventeen nephews," he told
everyone. "I have seventeen
nephews, and every single one will be
a sailor when he's grown!"

In every port he went to, he walked
up and down the streets. Clump-clump,
went his great sea boots.
He looked in the windows of the shops.
If he saw a parrot or a monkey
or a queer clock or a puzzle,
in he went.

"I'll take seventeen of those," he
said to the shopkeeper, pointing with
his finger. "Yes, sir, seventeen, for my
seventeen nephews who'll be sailors
when they're grown."

Seventeen of this . . .

Seventeen of that . . .

Seventeen surprises from every port!
What a fine lot of surprises
that sailor had, to take home
to his seventeen nephews!

But he did have a niece. She was
a very small niece, with pigtails and
freckles. She could never be a sailor
when she grew up.

"I know I can't be a sailor," she
said, "but my uncle is a sailor. He's
a very big sailor, and he may bring
me a pug dog when he comes home
from sea."

Her uncle never did. He just
brought—

Seventeen of this . . .

Seventeen of that . . .

Seventeen of everything for his
seventeen nephews who were sure to
be sailors.

When he had given out the presents, the big, merry sailor always got seventeen thank-you's.

Then he would see his one small niece standing in the corner.

"Who are you?" he always asked.

The very small niece said, "I'm the one niece. I think you always forget, Uncle, you have one niece."

"Oh, no," said the sailor. But he always looked sad, because he *had* forgotten. He would reach in his pocket and find a strange coin. He always gave the strange coin to his one small niece and said, "There, that's for you!"

The very small niece kept all the coins. She had a whole bag full. But they weren't parrots or monkeys or puzzles or clocks.

And they surely weren't a small pug dog.

"Next time," the niece thought. "Next time, maybe." But next time, no.

Seventeen of this . . .

And next time, no.

Seventeen of that . . . for the seventeen nephews. For the niece, the big, merry sailor had only a coin and a pat.

One day the very small niece cleaned all the coins. She put them in the bag and waited for her uncle.

In he came with his seventeen of this and his seventeen of that. And nothing for the niece except—

"Who are you?" And another strange coin . . .

But the niece said, "No, thank you, Uncle. I have lots of coins . . . Will you take them with you? And when you get to China will you spend them for a pug dog I want very much?"

"I will," her uncle promised, "and this time I *won't* forget."

Then away went her uncle,
with a merry twinkle in his eyes.

"I have seventeen nephews," he told
everybody. "They'll all be sailors. And
I have one small niece. She has
pigtails and freckles, and she's
the apple of my eye."

And the minute his ship made any
port, he went straight to the shops
and got—

Eighteen of this . . .

Eighteen of that . . .

Eighteen presents from every port.
But just *one* from China . . .

And the one present from China
was a small pug dog for one small niece
with pigtails and freckles—who could
never be a sailor when she grew up.

Wish

If I could wish,
I'd be a fish
   (For just a day or two)
To flip and flash
And dart and splash
   And nothing else to do,
And never any one to say,
"Are you quite sure
   You washed today?"
I'd like it, wouldn't you?

Dorothy Brown Thompson

Just Suppose

Just suppose the milkman
   Brought us cake and bread.
Just suppose the postman
   Brought us milk instead.
Just suppose the breadman
   Brought us mail and money,
If everything were "just suppose,"
   Wouldn't that be funny?

—*Leland B. Jacobs*

155

A Cow in the House

Mabel Watts

Once there was a poor farmer.
He lived with his wife in a little
red house.

The little house had only two tiny
rooms, and a tiny porch on the side.

The farmer and his wife thought
their house was just the right size.
Then one morning the farmer's wife
made noodles.

The noodles were extra long, and
the kitchen was extra short. And there
the trouble began.

"If only we could buy a larger
house," said the farmer's wife.

And she fussed and she fretted
the whole morning long.

"We have no money to buy a larger house," said the farmer. So away he went to tell his trouble to Grandpa Wiseman.

"If you will do just as I tell you," said Grandpa Wiseman, "then everything will turn out all right."

"Indeed I will," said the farmer.

"First," said the old man, "you must take your hen into the house."

So the farmer went home, and he took his hen into the house.

The hen had never been in a house before. She did not know how to behave. She jumped up on the table and onto the farmer's lap.

At last the farmer could stand it no longer. He went to see Grandpa Wiseman.

Grandpa Wiseman said, "Now you must take the goat into the house."

So the farmer went home and took his goat into the house.

The goat ate the curtains. She slept on the bed. She smashed the chairs. She fought with the hen.

So back went the farmer to tell Grandpa Wiseman about it.

"Both the hen and the goat need company," said the old man. "Now you must go home and take your pig into the house."

"Oh, no," said the farmer, "not the pig!"

"Yes," said Grandpa Wiseman, "the pig!"

The pig took up a lot of room. He was more trouble than both the goat and the hen.

Everywhere the farmer's wife tried to put something, there was the pig.

Besides, the hen and the goat and the pig did not get along well together. Back went the farmer to tell Grandpa Wiseman about it.

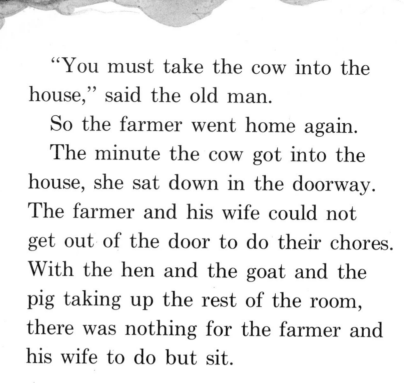

"You must take the cow into the house," said the old man.

So the farmer went home again.

The minute the cow got into the house, she sat down in the doorway. The farmer and his wife could not get out of the door to do their chores. With the hen and the goat and the pig taking up the rest of the room, there was nothing for the farmer and his wife to do but sit.

At last the farmer climbed out the window. He went to see Grandpa Wiseman.

"How are you getting along now?" asked the little old man.

"Well," said the farmer, "we're a little bit crowded. Still, it *could* be worse."

"How could it be worse?" said Grandpa Wiseman.

"Suppose my cousin and his wife and his ten children and their dog and cat should come and stay with us," said the farmer.

"Things would really be crowded then, wouldn't they?" laughed Grandpa Wiseman.

"Yes, indeed," said the farmer, "things can always get a little bit worse."

"Now we're getting somewhere with your problem," said Grandpa Wiseman. "Run home now, and push the cow out of the house."

"By all means!" said the farmer. He could hardly wait to get home.

It was simply wonderful having
the cow out of the way. The farmer
told Grandpa Wiseman about it.

"Fine," said Grandpa Wiseman.
"Now drive the pig back into the
pigpen."

"Yes, indeed," said the farmer, and
he lost no time in doing as the old
man said.

"Does your house seem larger now?"
Grandpa Wiseman asked.

"Oh, yes," said the farmer. "We
have lots and lots of room now!"

"Fine," said the old man. "Now it is
time to turn out the goat."

Soon the goat was out in the yard
again. The house had never seemed
so large.

"We are beginning to rattle around like peas in a pod," the farmer told the old man.

"In that case," said Grandpa Wiseman, "you can let the hen out."

Now the little red house was just the right size for the farmer and his wife.

"I wouldn't want a larger house now," said the farmer's wife.

And away she went to the kitchen to make more noodles.

The noodles were still extra long, and the kitchen was still extra short. Still there was plenty of room in the little red house.

"It's all in knowing how to make the best of things," said the farmer. "And that's the truth!"

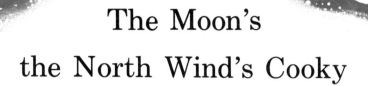

The Moon's
the North Wind's Cooky

The Moon's the North Wind's cooky,
He bites it, day by day,
Until there's but a rim of scraps
That crumble all away.
The South Wind is a baker.
He kneads clouds in his den,
And bakes a crisp new moon
     that . . . greedy
North . . . Wind . . . eats . . . again!

                   Vachel Lindsay

A Quail and a Snail

A handsome young quail
Was admiring his tail.
When along came a snail
Who started to wail.

"Why do you wail?"
Said the quail to the snail.
"I have no tail,"
Said the snail to the quail.

"You don't need a tail,"
Said the quail to the snail.
"I want a tail,"
Said the snail to the quail.

So the handsome young quail
Pulled out his tail
And using a nail
Tacked it on to the snail,

When along came a gale
And off sailed the snail.

And that was the end
Of the tail of the quail
And the end of the snail
And the end of this tale.

Polly Cameron

The White Goose

Tasha Tudor

The white goose was lost.

She had slipped away in the moonlight between the night and the dawn.

Robin missed her when he went to call the cows. The cows had not been waiting at the gate as usual.

The grass was silvery with frost and moonshine. Over the hill Robin could hear the cowbells. He could hear his own echo calling from the mist.

Robin could hear the calling of wild geese from the river. He stood still and listened. He had the feeling that something fell beside him.

He looked, and there on the grass lay a white feather. Beyond lay another white feather, and another.

Robin forgot about calling the cows. He forgot about the warm fire at home. He forgot about his mother cooking breakfast. All he saw were those white feathers lying in the moonlight. All he heard was the calling of wild geese from the river.

Robin turned off the cow path.
Down across the pasture, through
the woods, down to the marsh, he ran.

There he stopped. Beyond lay the
river.

The honking of geese was deafening.
Then, all was still. Robin looked
through the tall grasses.

There they were, the wild geese.

Among them stood a little girl,
stroking their sleek necks. She looked
up and laughed at Robin.

Robin felt the cold moonlight run
through him as he listened to the
girl's fairy laughter. He felt the dark
eyes of the wild geese watching him.

The little girl walked toward him.
"Come," said she, and took his hand.

Again Robin felt the cold touch of
moonlight, and shivered.

"Come quickly," said the little girl.
"It will soon be daylight. Here is
a fine gander. Jump on his back and
fly away with us."

"Fly away with us!" echoed the
geese.

Robin hesitated. "I am thinking of home," said he.

"I know," said the little girl, "but come. We will fly over great forests and mighty rivers. All the birds of the air will talk to us."

But still Robin hesitated. "I can see my little sister smiling in her cradle," said he.

"I know," said the little girl, "but come. We will fly up that beam of moonlight to the most wonderful place you ever heard of. We will fly to the hidden side of the moon."

"The hidden side of the moon," echoed the geese.

"I can hear my mother singing in the kitchen. I cannot come," said Robin.

Then Robin saw tears running down the little girl's face. She turned sadly away and faded into the mist.

In her place stood the little white goose.

Then all the geese rose into the air on thundering wings. Robin was left alone, standing in the moonlight.

    *   *   *   *

Now some say that people with pointed ears, like Robin's, see things that aren't really there.

Maybe if you had pointed ears you, too, might hear that little girl's laughter and look into her fairy face. You might even fly up that beam of moonlight to the hidden side of the moon. Who knows!

Strange things are said to happen when the wild geese fly in the moonlight between night and dawning.

The Old Woman and the Strawberry Tarts

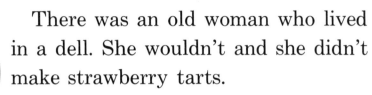

Gertrude Crampton

There was an old woman who lived
in a dell. She wouldn't and she didn't
make strawberry tarts.

She made tarts of lemon, and she
made them of lime. She made them
of pumpkin, and she made them
of peach.

But she wouldn't and she didn't
make strawberry tarts.

Every morning she packed her tarts
in a basket and carried them off
to the baker's shop.

Every morning the baker counted
the lemon tarts and the lime tarts,
the pumpkin tarts and the peach tarts.
He wished the old woman would make
strawberry tarts for him to sell.

"Not I," said the old woman, with
a toss of her head and her skirts.

And home she went.

"It may be," said the baker to himself, "that the old woman has no strawberries. Having no strawberries is a good reason for not making strawberry tarts."

So the baker bought all the strawberries in the town and took them to the old woman.

Later in the day, the baker got on his bicycle and rode out to the dell. He had to see how the old woman was getting along with the strawberry tarts.

But she was making strawberry jam.

And she wouldn't and she didn't make strawberry tarts.

"Maybe the old woman is very fond of strawberry jam," thought the baker. "But if she had many, many strawberries, she might have enough left over to make strawberry tarts."

Early the next morning the baker bought two hundred strawberry plants.

Then he rode his bicycle out to the dell and helped the woman plant all the fine strawberry plants.

The days went by, and the weeks went by. The rains fell, and the sun shone. The flowers bloomed, and the petals fell. And the baker dreamed of strawberry tarts.

At last the strawberries began to ripen. The baker could wait no longer. He had to see how the old woman was getting along with the strawberry tarts. So he rode his bicycle out to the dell.

But when he got there, she was making strawberry shortcake.

And she didn't and she wouldn't make strawberry tarts.

"Not I," said the old woman, with a toss of her head and her skirts.

The baker started home. But he got no farther than the edge of the dell when a question popped into his head.

So he rode back into the dell.

"Why?" asked the baker, very firm, very stern, very puffed-out-in-the-chest.

"Because I don't know how," said the old woman, very meek and very mild.

"Why didn't you tell me before?" asked the baker.

"Because you never did ask me," said the old woman, not so meek and not so mild.

So the baker got on his bicycle. He rode like the wind to town and back.

Then he took out of his hat his great grandmother's very best recipe for making strawberry tarts.

The old woman got the first batch baked in time for supper. The baker said, "They are as good as my great grandmother's best strawberry tarts. No—they are even better."

So the old woman who lived in the dell said she would bake strawberry tarts. She would bake them for the baker to sell.

And she would and she did.
For she could!

Blum

Dog means dog,
And cat means cat,
And there are lots
Of words like that.

A cart's a cart,
To pull or shove,
A plate's a plate,
To eat off of.

But there are other
Words I say
When I am left
Alone to play.

Blum is one.
Blum is a word
That very few
Have ever heard.

I like to say it,
"Blum, blum, blum"—
I do it loud
Or in a hum.

All by itself,
It's nice to sing:
It does not mean
A single thing.

Dorothy Aldis

183

A Good Man
and His Good Wife

Ruth Krauss

Once there was a good man and he had a good wife.

They lived in a beautiful cottage. It had white walls and red curtains and lots of little cubbyholes and handy shelves.

The man and his wife were very happy, except that he could never find things.

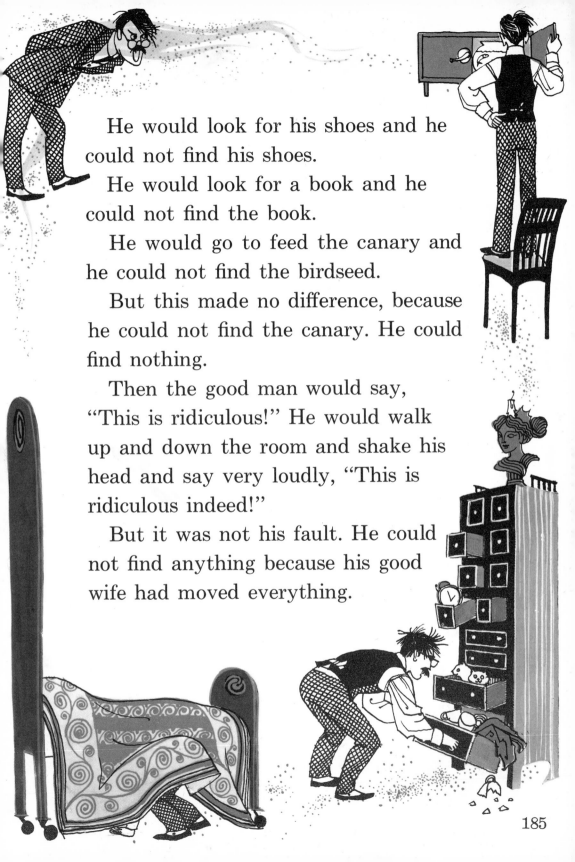

He would look for his shoes and he could not find his shoes.

He would look for a book and he could not find the book.

He would go to feed the canary and he could not find the birdseed.

But this made no difference, because he could not find the canary. He could find nothing.

Then the good man would say, "This is ridiculous!" He would walk up and down the room and shake his head and say very loudly, "This is ridiculous indeed!"

But it was not his fault. He could not find anything because his good wife had moved everything.

She would move the parlor table
from the middle of the parlor
to a corner of the kitchen. She would
move the kitchen table from the
middle of the kitchen to under
an apple tree in the garden.

She would say, "My dear, I get so
tired of the same things in the same
places." Then she would stand back
and admire her work.

She moved the clock from the wall
above the bed to an end of the shelf
in the parlor.

She moved her good man's Sunday
clothes from the closet in the hall
to the closet in the attic.

She moved his favorite chair from
its place before the fire to a corner
of the bedroom.

She moved everything in the little
house.

She said, "Yes, yes, I do get so tired
of the same things in the same
places!"

Then the good man had to learn
where things were all over again.

But by the time he learned to find
his fishing rod in the broom closet
next to the pantry, everything was
changed again.

Again he looked very stern and
cried, "This is ridiculous!"

He decided to do something
about it. He said, "I will do something
about it," and smiled to himself. He
said, "I'll settle this once and for all."

And he did something about it.

He put his shoe on his head.

He wore his garters around his neck.

He tied his necktie around his knee.

He wore his trousers for his coat
and his coat for his trousers, and both
of them upside down.

He wore his spectacles on his elbow.

He wore his socks on his ears.

Then he crawled downstairs.

He sat on the breakfast table, ate
his napkin, and wiped his face
on a biscuit.

When his good wife saw him, she opened her eyes wide. She dropped the dishes. She opened her mouth wide in surprise. She threw up her hands.

Then she cried, "My dear, this is ridiculous!"

He did not reply, but went on buttering his napkin and chewing little pieces off it, and wiping his face with the biscuit. His garters jingled around his neck, and his socks flopped on his ears.

Then she cried again, "But, truly, this is ridiculous, this is just too ridiculous!"

"But, my dear," he said very quietly, "I get so tired of the same things in the same places."

So that was how the good man cured his good woman of a bad habit.

And they lived even more happily than before in their beautiful cottage with its white walls and red curtains and little cubbyholes and handy shelves. Nowadays when the good man wants to read a book, he knows that he will find it in the bookcase.

ACKNOWLEDGMENTS

The editors wish to extend their thanks and appreciation to the following authors, publishers, and periodicals for kindly granting us permission to reprint selections in this volume.

ABELARD-SCHUMAN LIMITED for BIRD TALK from *Up the Windy Hill* by Aileen Fisher. Copyright 1953 by Aileen Fisher.—CHILD LIFE for THE WISH by Ann Friday. Copyright 1955 by Child Life.—CHILDRENS PRESS, INC. for CITY BOY by Miriam Schlein. Copyright 1955 by Miriam Schlein. MARCHETTE CHUTE for THE DOORMAN from *Rhymes About the City*. Copyright 1946 by Marchette Chute.—WM. COLLINS SONS & CO., LTD. for WASHING from *More About Me* by John Drinkwater.—COWARD MCCANN, INC. for A QUAIL AND A SNAIL from *A Child's Book of Nonsense* by Polly Cameron. Copyright 1960 by Polly Cameron.—PAT DAY for THE MOUSE'S HOUSE from *Jack and Jill*. Copyright 1956 by The Curtis Publishing Company.—DOUBLEDAY & COMPANY, INC. for UNCLE FRANK from *Goose Grass Rhymes* by Monica Shannon. Copyright 1954.—FOLLETT PUBLISHING COMPANY for A COW IN THE HOUSE by Mabel Watts. Copyright 1956 by Follett Publishing Company.—GOLDEN PRESS, INC. for the following selections, copyright in the years indicated by Golden Press, Inc.: THE OLD WOMAN AND THE STRAWBERRY TARTS from *The Golden Funny Book* by Gertrude Crampton (1950); SEVENTEEN NEPHEWS from *Pirates, Ships and Sailors* by Kathryn and Byron Jackson (1950); THE WILD WHITE HORSE and HOW THE CHIPMUNK GOT HIS STRIPES from the Giant Little Golden Book *Cowboys and Indians* by Willis Lindquist (1958); RUSTY'S ADVENTURE by Seymour Reit (1965); BIG IS A CITY and LITTLE IS A TOWN by Dorothy Hall Smith (1962); THE DOG AND THE ROOSTER from *Nursery Tales,* edited by Elsa Jane Werner (1952); HARCOURT, BRACE & WORLD, INC. for THE NEW LITTLE BOY from *Windy Morning* by Harry Behn. Copyright 1953 by Harry Behn; and MY OTHER NAME from *Whispers* by Myra Cohn Livingston. Copyright 1958 by Myra Cohn Livingston.—HENRY HOLT AND COMPANY, INC. for THE STORY THAT NEVER ENDS from *A Rocket in My Pocket* by Carl Withers. Copyright 1948 by Henry Holt and Company, Inc.—HOUGHTON MIFFLIN for I MET A MAN WITH THREE EYES from *I Met A Man* by John Ciardi. Copyright 1961.—LOTHROP, LEE AND SHEPARD CO., INC. for THE WONDERFUL FEAST by Esphyr Slobodkina. Copyright 1955 by Lothrop, Lee and Shepard Co., Inc.; and RAINDROP SPLASH from the book of the same title by Alvin Tresselt. Copyright 1946 by Lothrop, Lee and Shepard Co., Inc.—THE MACMILLAN CO. for THE MOON'S THE NORTH WIND'S COOKY from *Collected Poems by Vachel Lindsay*. Copyright 1914 by The Macmillan Co., renewed 1942 by Elizabeth C. Lindsay.—THE MEDICI SOCIETY LTD. and G. P. PUTNAM'S SONS for EVERYBODY SAYS from *Everything and Anything* by Dorothy Aldis. Copyright 1927 by Minton, Balch & Co., renewed 1955 by Dorothy Aldis.—G. P. PUTNAM'S SONS for BLUM from *All Together* by Dorothy Aldis. Copyright 1952 by G. P. Putnam's Sons.—STORY PARADE, INC. for ONE COLD DAY by Elizabeth Coatsworth. Copyright 1952 by Story Parade, Inc.—FREDERICK WARNE & CO., INC. for SUSAN BLUE by Kate Greenaway, from *Marigold Garden*. Copyright 1910 by Frederick Warne, Inc.